Sally

School Is My World

SPARKLER BOOKS
AN IMPRINT OF PHAROS BOOKS • A SCRIPPS HOWARD COMPANY
NEW YORK

LMC

Originally published and produced by
Arnoldo Mondadori Editore S.p.A., Milano

© 1988 United Feature Syndicate, Inc.
All rights reserved.
Based on the Italian Language Book
''Sally, la mia scuola e il mondo''
(© 1987 United Feature Syndicate, Inc.)

LC 88-042735   88- 10826
ISBN 0-88687-374-6

Printed in Italy

Sparkler Books
An Imprint of Pharos Books
A Scripps Howard Company
200 Park Avenue
New York, NY 10166

10   9   8   7   6   5   4   3   2   1

CONTENTS

Sally's brother Charlie Brown was so pleased and proud when she was born that he passed out chocolate cigars. Since then, he's been trying to understand her. She always looks for the easy way out, especially at school, where her view of life reflects the confusion and frustration kids often feel. She has a schoolgirl crush on Linus, her "Sweet Baboo"; and although she may never win Linus' heart, she has her big brother wrapped around her little finger. Writing letters or doing her homework, she has an uninhibited view of the world that is painful and lovable at the same time. That's our Sally.

Presenting... Sally

© 1967 United Feature Syndicate, Inc.

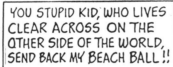

© 1972 United Feature Syndicate, Inc.

© 1971 United Feature Syndicate, Inc.

NO! NO! NO! NO! NO! NO! NO! NO! NO! NO! NO! NO! NO!

Sally and School

Sally in Class

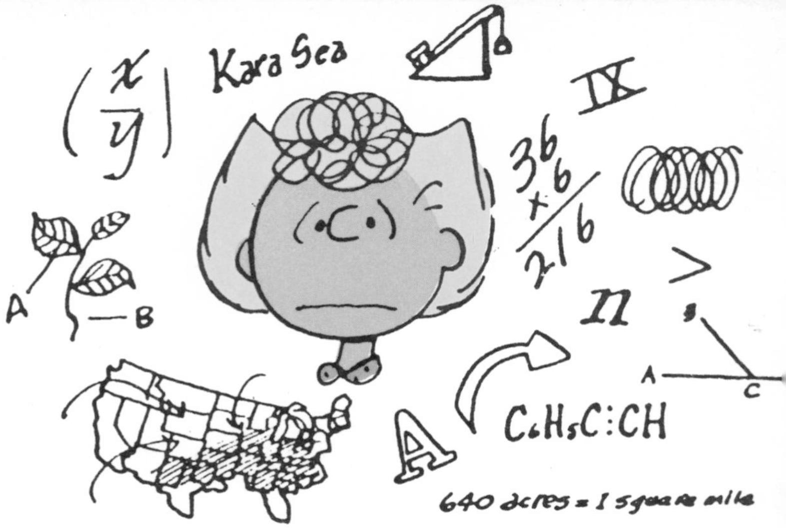

Kara Sea
36
x 6
216
IX
A
B
n
A
C
$C_6H_5C{:}CH$
640 acres = 1 square mile

YES, MA'AM? MY NAME?
MY NAME IS SALLY BROWN, AND I HATE SCHOOL!
© 1969 United Feature Syndicate, Inc.
PLEASE, DON'T CRY...
SCHULZ

THE ANSWER IS TWELVE!
IT ISN'T? HOW ABOUT SIX?
© 1971 United Feature Syndicate, Inc.
FOUR? NINE? TWO? TEN?
DO YOU HAVE THE FEELING THAT I'M GUESSING?
SCHULZ

© 1975 United Feature Syndicate, Inc.
MA'AM, I HAVE A SUGGESTION FOR A CLASS PROJECT..
WHY DON'T WE ALL GET TOGETHER, AND RAISE A RUCKUS? THEY'RE EASY TO RAISE...ALL YOU HAVE TO DO IS SHOUT, AND THEY GROW!
AHAHAHAHAH!
YES, MA'AM...
SCHULZ

IT HAS BEEN FORTY-FIVE MINUTES SINCE I FIRST CAME INTO SCHOOL THIS MORNING...

I FIND, UNFORTUNATELY, THAT I AM NOT ANY SMARTER NOW THAN WHEN I ARRIVED....IF IT IS TRUE THAT NATURE ABHORS A VACUUM, I MAY EVEN BE A LITTLE DUMBER!! NOW, THEREFORE, I WOULD LIKE TO...

YES, MA'AM?

RATS! I HAD A PRETTY GOOD SPEECH GOING THERE FOR A MINUTE!

© 1973 United Feature Syndicate, Inc.

WELL, HERE I AM AGAIN FOR "SHOW AND TELL"

AND GUESS WHAT I'VE BROUGHT TODAY! I HAVE THINGS IN HERE TO THRILL YOU AND CHILL YOU! I HAVE THINGS IN HERE TO FILL YOU WITH FEAR, WITH TERROR, WITH HORROR! I HAVE THINGS IN HERE TO...

...YES, MA'AM?

ALL THE LIFE HAS GONE OUT OF "SHOW AND TELL"

© 1972 United Feature Syndicate, Inc.

DRAW A FARM? YOU WANT US TO DRAW A FARM?

© 1969 United Feature Syndicate, Inc.

I CAN'T DRAW A FARM.. I'VE NEVER EVEN **SEEN** A FARM! BESIDES, COWS' LEGS ARE IMPOSSIBLE TO DRAW...

I DEFY ANYONE IN THIS CLASS TO DRAW A GOOD COW LEG!

I'M THE ONLY PERSON I KNOW WHO'S FAILING FIRST-GRADE ART..

PRINCIPAL'S OFFICE

17

18

FIRST THEY WANT YOU TO SHOW AND TELL, AND THEN THEY DON'T WANT YOU TO SHOW AND TELL...

Sally Gives a Report

Sally and Homework

English Theme

I hate writing English themes.

I hate it! I hate it! I hate it!

And now for the theme itself...

Report:

"What I enjoyed most about our field trip"

The girls got to wear slacks.

History Report —

The Egyptians.

Family life among the Egyptians was easier than it is today.

They were all facing the same way.

Sally Does Homework with the Rest of the Gang

"I can give you three ships, Mr. Day," said the Queen.

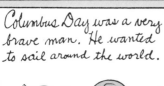

27

$1 < 5$

AHAHAHAHAH YAK YAK YAK!

28

Sally at Summer Camp

© 1985 United Feature Syndicate, Inc.

© 1985 United Feature Syndicate, Inc.

© 1985 United Feature Syndicate, Inc.

8903161

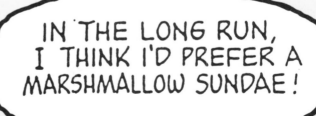

Sally and Charlie Brown

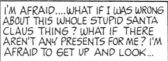

32

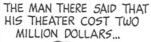

34

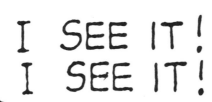
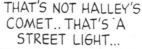

DAD SAYS WHEN HE WAS LITTLE, ICE CREAM CONES WERE ONLY A DIME..

I SEE THEY HAVE BUTTER PECAN..

WHAT IF I ORDER IT, AND DON'T LIKE IT?

YOU COULD TRY PISTACHIO ALMOND

WHAT IF I ORDER IT, AND DON'T LIKE IT?

HOW ABOUT MINT CHOCOLATE CHIP?

WHAT IF I ORDER IT, AND DON'T LIKE IT?

I THINK I'D BETTER JUST HAVE VANILLA

WHAT'S THE MATTER?

I DON'T LIKE IT!

Sally and Linus

PUNT!

I WAS WONDERING WHAT WAS INSIDE IT...

HERE, SALLY... HAPPY VALENTINE'S DAY...

© 1969 United Feature Syndicate, Inc.

WHAAH!

EXCUSE ME... A TEAR CAME TO MY EYE!

I'LL NEVER GET TO THE FIRST GRADE

I'M ALMOST SURE THEY'RE GOING TO MAKE ME GO THROUGH KINDERGARTEN AGAIN

WHY?

I FAILED FLOWER-BRINGING!!

38

Sally and Snoopy

 STUPID BEAGLE!

 ALL BECAUSE OF YOU, I FAILED SHOW AN' TELL!

NOW, I'LL PROBABLY GET BAD GRADES ALL YEAR AND NEVER BE A GOOD STUDENT AND NOT GET INTO THE COLLEGE OF MY CHOICE!

 SMAK! POOR, SWEET BABY!

 TODAY FOR "SHOW AND TELL" I HAVE BROUGHT MY BROTHER'S DOG...

 WHICH MAY TURN OUT TO BE THE BIGGEST MISTAKE OF MY LIFE!

 LIFT ME HIGHER..WHEN HALLEY'S COMET COMES BY, I WANT TO SEE IT..

 OKAY, NOW HAND ME THE BINOCULARS

 AAUGH!

 STUPID BEAGLE!!

Sally and the Rest
of the Gang

I WISH I HAD A SECRET ADMIRER...

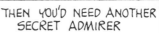

SOMEONE WHO WOULD SEND ME FLOWERS AND LITTLE NOTES AND THINGS LIKE THAT...

AND THEN, ALL OF A SUDDEN, HE WOULD TELL ME WHO HE WAS...

THEN YOU'D NEED ANOTHER SECRET ADMIRER

I REMEMBER THE CEREAL BOWL I HAD WHEN I WAS LITTLE..

I ALSO REMEMBER THE STROLLER THAT MOM USED TO PUSH ME IN, AND I REMEMBER THE PARK WE'D ALWAYS GO TO...

I REMEMBER MY FIRST RIDE ON A BUS AND THE FIRST TIME I EVER RODE AN ESCALATOR..

I HAVE A GOOD REMEMBERY!

SCHOOL STARTS AGAIN NEXT WEEK...

I THINK I'VE RUINED HER EYES FOR GOOD!